WORLD'S WORST...

CHEMICAL Disasters

Rob Alcraft

Heinemann
LIBRARY

H **www.heinemann.co.uk**
Visit our website to find out more information about **Heinemann Library** books.

To order:
☎ Phone 44 (0) 1865 888066
🖹 Send a fax to 44 (0) 1865 314091
💻 Visit the Heinemann Bookshop at www.heinemann.co.uk to browse our catalogue and order online.

First published in Great Britain by Heinemann Library,
Halley Court, Jordan Hill, Oxford OX2 8EJ
a division of Reed Educational and Professional Publishing Ltd.

Heinemann is a registered trademark of Reed Educational & Professional Publishing Ltd.

OXFORD MELBOURNE AUCKLAND JOHANNESBURG BLANTYRE GABORONE IBADAN PORTSMOUTH (NH) USA CHICAGO

Designed by Celia Floyd
Illustrations by David Cuzik (Pennant Illustration) and Jeff Edwards
Originated by Dot Gradations, UK
Printed by Wing King Tong, in Hong Kong

ISBN 0 431 01285 7 (hardback)   ISBN 0 431 01292 X (paperback)
04 03 02 01 00   04 03 02 01 00
10 9 8 7 6 5 4 3 2   10 9 8 7 6 5 4 3 2 1

British Library Cataloguing in Publication Data

Alcraft, Rob, 1966–
World's worst chemical disasters
1. Chemicals – Accidents – Juvenile literature
I. Title II. Chemical disasters
363.1'7

Acknowledgements
The Publishers would like to thank the following for permission to reproduce photographs: Ann Ronan: p7; Corbis: Bettman p.15, p.19, Rainier p.24, Yamashita p.12; Heinemann: p.18; Hulton Getty: p.14; Rex Features: SIPA p.9, p.21; Science Photo Library: Perquis p.5, Garry Watson p.6: Telegraph Colour Library: Bora Merdsoy p.29; Tony Stone: Wayne Eastep p.2, Keith Wood p.26, David Woodfall p.27.

Cover photograph reproduced with permission of Tony Stone: David Woodfall.

Our thanks to Dr Henry Wilson of the International Journal of Disaster Prevention and Management, Department of Industrial Technology, University of Bradford for his comments in the preparation of this book.

Every effort has been made to contact copyright holders of any material reproduced in this book. Any omissions will be rectified in subsequent printings if notice is given to the Publisher.

Any words appearing in the text in bold, **like this**, are explained in the Glossary.

Contents

A Chemical World

We live in a world of chemicals. There are over 60,000 artificial chemicals in everyday use. All sorts of plastics, our clothes, and even our food are made and coloured with chemicals. Chemicals make the medicines which make us better. They help us keep our homes clean. Farmers use them as **fertilizer**, and to kill pests and weeds.

When chemicals are mixed or heated they make new substances. Chemical factories make and mix chemicals to make acids and dyes used in many kinds of industry. The most common **raw materials** for making chemicals are oil and coal.

Farmers spray fields of crops with chemical **pesticides** and fertilizers to produce greater yields. But these chemicals can be harmful to the **environment**.

Rubber gloves on a factory production line. Like many chemicals, **synthetic** rubber is made from oil, gas and coal.

In many countries there are laws saying how chemicals can be made. The **World Health Organization** – an international organization which is part of the **United Nations** – checks the safety of chemical industries around the world. It also monitors accidents and spills, and how people are affected. Chemical factories have to be safe. Workers have to be trained so they know what to do in an emergency. Many countries also have inspectors who check chemical factories.

Acids and alkalis

There are two families of chemicals – acids and alkalis. Lemons contain acid, which is why they have a sharp, sour taste. Strong acids are very dangerous, even to touch. They burn the skin and can eat through wood, cloth and metal. Acids are used in many industries. They are in batteries, **explosives** and fertilizers.

Alkalis are soapy to the touch, though strong alkalis will also burn your skin. Alkalis are used in soap and to make glass.

5

Handle with Care

Chemicals are useful, but they can also be dangerous. Many are poisonous and cause unpleasant diseases and illnesses. Many can burn fiercely, and are highly **explosive**. If they are not used properly, they can kill.

Because many chemicals are so dangerous even small mistakes and accidents can be disastrous. Even very small amounts of some chemicals can be harmful if released into air or water. Chemicals are often invisible, making them hard to detect. If they leak into the **environment**, they can build up over many years. The effects of a chemical disaster can take many years to show up. The first sign can be when people become ill, or a river or forest dies.

The skull and crossbones symbol means danger – in this case chemical danger.

Dangerous chemicals

Your body – a chemical factory

Our bodies contain chemicals. The way in which they react and work together is controlled by **enzymes**, which keep our bodies working properly. Your body contains around 30,000 enzymes, making it one of the most complicated chemical factories around.

In this book we look at three of the world's worst chemical disasters. These are disasters that shocked the world, and in many ways changed the view of safety in the chemical industry for good. We look minute by minute at what happened, and what went wrong. Have the lessons been learned that will avoid disaster next time?

This line drawing by John Tenniel is from the 1965 edition of *Alice's Adventures in Wonderland* by Lewis Carroll.

Mad as a hatter?

Remember the Mad-Hatter from *Alice's Adventures in Wonderland*? In the past hat makers really did go mad. They used materials treated with chemicals that contained poisonous mercury. After years breathing in mercury **fumes**, the nervous systems of many hat makers were affected, and they would shake and slur their words.

Poison!
The Poisoning of Minamata Bay, Japan

In 1932 a plastics factory in Minamata Bay, Japan began dumping its **toxic** mercury waste into the sea. It was the beginning of a pollution disaster that was to kill hundreds of people, and disable thousands more.

Death by pollution

First the fish began to die. They littered Minamata Bay's shining blue waters, and washed up on the beaches. But no-one knew why. Next cats and crows began dying.

Then in 1953 people began to complain of strange illnesses. They had slurred speech and they were dizzy. Slowly people began to die. When doctors examined the bodies they found that the victims' brains had been damaged. But they had no idea what caused the damage. They named the mysterious illness Minamata Disease.

As the deaths continued only a company called Chisso Co Ltd knew the facts. The people of Minamata Bay were being poisoned by mercury waste from the Chisso plastics factory. In 1956 the Chisso Company doctor examined cats which had consumed waste water from the factory. He discovered that mercury in the water had killed them. But executives at the factory ordered the cats and the evidence to be destroyed, and carried on pumping the mercury waste into the waters of Minamata Bay.

Many of the victims of the Minamata Bay disaster were unborn children. They were poisoned in the womb, from food eaten by their mothers. Mrs Sakamoto's daughter, Shinobu, was poisoned by mercury.

We took her to the hospital. By then the cause of the poisoning was known. I was told there was no cure. We could only try to train her to use the undamaged parts of her body and brain.

At first our only hope was that she could walk. Then, we prayed that she could go to school. Now our hope is that she will be able to take care of herself when we no longer can.

A poisonous metal

Mercury is a potentially lethal poison. It can cause illness, madness and eventually death. It gets into the body through the skin, through **fumes**, or through **contaminated** food. In the Minamata Bay disaster, fish and shellfish in the bay absorbed the mercury from the factory waste. Fishermen and their families became ill when they ate the fish.

Contaminated water and waste gushed freely into Minamata Bay.

The Making of a Disaster

Chisso Co Ltd knew that the mercury it was dumping into Minamata Bay was killing sea life and the people and animals that fed on it. Yet they carried on dumping water containing mercury into the bay until 1968.

It was a slow, lingering disaster. Around 900 people died. More than 12,000 people were affected. Children were born sick and disabled.

1   In 1932 Chisso Co Ltd begins releasing mercury into Minamata Bay.

2   The first fish begin to die in the 1950s. Tests on crabs and fish in the bay find that they are **contaminated** with large amounts of mercury. Cats and birds which eat the fish from the polluted bay start dying.

3   **Bacteria** in Minamata Bay change the mercury waste into methyl mercury. Methyl mercury is even more deadly than mercury itself.

4   In 1956, after people and animals begin to die, a doctor at Chisso Co Ltd traces the causes of Minamata Disease to mercury in Chisso's own factory waste. Nothing is done. The Japan Chemical Industry Association helps Chisso by supplying scientists to find other reasons for Minamata Disease – reasons that do not blame Chisso.

7 The town of Minamata is scarred by the disaster. Thousands of people leave, and a population of 50,000 shrinks to around 32,000. The fishing industry, which many people rely on, is destroyed.

6 In 1966 Chisso finally stops dumping mercury waste in Minamata Bay. The national government does not officially blame Chisso for the disaster until 1968. The government itself never accepts responsibility.

5 In late 1956, the Japanese government officially recognizes the link between eating fish from Minamata Bay and Minamata Disease. Nothing is done.

The 65-Year Clean-Up

Official reaction to the Minamata disaster was slow. It took the Japanese government 11 years to officially blame Chisso Co Ltd for the pollution. It took another 20 years before trials and appeals in the courts met with any success. It wasn't until 1995 that Japan's Supreme Court found the President of the Chisso Company and the director of the Chisso Minamata factory guilty of causing the disaster.

These victims of the Minamata Bay disaster were comparatively lucky. Although they suffer from extreme disability, they are alive, and able to enjoy this outing to see the spring cherry blossoms.

A company town

The town of Minamata depended for most of it jobs on the Chisso Company factory. One third of all the employed people in the town worked there. Nearly two-thirds of local taxes also came from the factory. Most of Minamata's councillors and mayors had once been workers or managers at the Chisso factory. These facts meant that at first no-one really wanted to criticize the Chisso Company – even if it was suspected of poisoning Minamata Bay.

Blame was very important in the Minamata disaster. It meant that managers at Chisso had to take responsibility for what they had done. It meant Chisso had to pay **compensation** to those who had suffered, and pay to clean the poisoned sea. In 1995 Chisso Co Ltd agreed to pay out 4.94 billion Japanese yen to five groups of patients. Yet not everyone is being compensated. Although 12,615 people are Minamata Disease sufferers, only 3000 have been officially recognized as such, and paid compensation. It seems many victims will never get the justice they deserve.

Cleaning Minamata Bay

The cleaning of Minamata Bay took many years. In 1974 a 2-km long net was stretched across the bay to trap fish. This prevented poisoned catches finding their way onto people's plates. In 1977 some poisoned sludge was removed. Then in 1983 another project to **dredge** the poisonous mud from the bay began. Only if it was removed would the **environment** recover, and people be safe from poisoning. Finally, in 1997, fish from Minamata Bay were officially declared safe to eat. Nets trapping fish inside the bay were taken away – 65 years after the pollution began.

Knowing and complaining

As people in Japan began to hear of Minamata Disease, they began to worry about pollution in their own areas. The Environment Agency of the **OECD** found that in 1960 very few complaints were made to the authorities about pollution. By 1972 86,000 complaints were being made. People had begun to realize the dangers of pollution, and wanted something done about it.

Explosion!
The Destruction of Texas City, USA

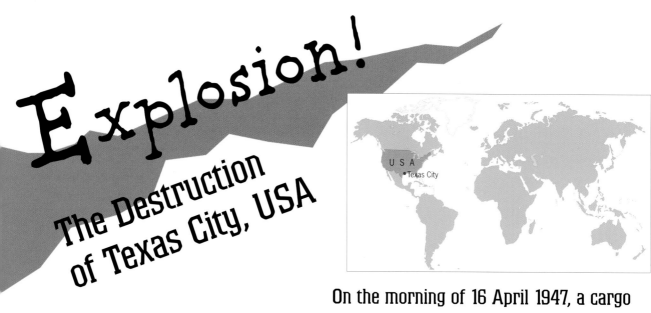

On the morning of 16 April 1947, a cargo ship in Texas City harbour, USA caught fire and exploded. Over 500 people died. More than 50 years later the people of Texas City still remember what they call simply 'the explosion'.

No ordinary day

It was a cool clear morning. The harbour at Texas City was busy with ships. It seemed like any ordinary day. But one ship would shortly change everything. It was the *Grandcamp*, bound for Europe. Shortly before 9am it caught fire. Thick black smoke began to billow out across the water.

In the explosion at Texas City Harbour a huge steel barge was blown from the ship basin to dry land, taking with it several cars.

On the quay a crowd gathered to watch. 27 fire-fighters from the Texas City Volunteer Fire Department arrived to tackle the blaze. As the smoke shifted in the breeze, people saw it was a curious orange colour. This was the first sign of disaster.

The *Grandcamp* was carrying nitrate **fertilizer**. It would burn, and then explode. The burning ship was a time bomb. Suddenly, a little after 9am, the *Grandcamp* exploded. Smoke shot 600m into the air. The blast smashed across the harbour, sending a tidal wave crashing into the town. Entire buildings collapsed in flames. A chemical plant, warehouses and **refineries** began to burn. Texas City was going up in flames.

> *I had just gotten out of bed when I felt the house shaking to beat the band. I thought I saw bodies wheeling through whole bunch of debris in the air. [Then I saw] a dark ridge (the shock wave from the blast) moving 3m off the ground, heading toward the house.*
>
> John Hill, a chemical engineer working at a plant in Texas City on the morning of the explosion.

This chemical plant was one of the buildings devastated by the Texas City blaze.

Texas City Just Blew Up!

Fires started everywhere. All day Texas City burned. Fire-fighters and rescuers struggled to find and treat survivors, and to fight the fires which raged throughout the city. Frank Simpson, a student outside the city was told, 'Texas City just blew up'.

But the disaster wasn't over. Out in the wrecked harbour another ship, the *High Flyer* was burning. On board was more **explosive** nitrate. Tugs struggled to tow the *High Flyer* out into the sea, but it was stuck on wreckage from the first explosion. Night came and the ship burned on. At 1.10am the *High Flyer* – still in the harbour – finally exploded. More fires burned in the city.

1 Warehouses and **refineries** ring the harbour. The *Grandcamp*, bound for Europe, is loaded with nitrate **fertilizer**. When the fire starts no-one knows its cargo is dangerous. Crowds gather to watch the fire.

2 The *Grandcamp*'s steam fire control system is switched on. But instead of smothering the fire, the heat and pressure react with the nitrate cargo, producing explosive gas.

3 *Grandcamp*'s entire cargo explodes. The blast wrecks the harbour. Debris flies into the air. A chemical plant starts burning. More explosions threaten. Almost all the fire equipment in Texas City is destroyed in the first blast. Many of the volunteer fire-fighters at the scene are killed.

6 Fire burns through Texas City for a week after the disaster. A month goes by before the last body is pulled clear of the collapsed buildings. Many of the dead are never identified.

5 Out in the harbour the *High Flyer* is on fire. It is also carrying an explosive cargo of nitrate. Tugs try to pull it clear of the harbour, but fail. At 1am people are ordered clear. At 1.10am the ship explodes. This explosion is larger and more devastating than the first.

4 Beyond the harbour a wave of water from the blast crashes into the town. Buildings crumble in the blast and begin to burn. The *Grandcamp*'s 1.5 tonne anchor is blasted into an oil refinery 3km away. The explosion is heard 240km away.

Getting Justice

Fires and explosions had become part of normal life in Texas City. It was a booming industrial town. The harbour was ringed by **refineries**, warehouses and chemical works. When oil tanks or warehouses went up in flames people would flock to see them. It was public entertainment. Safety wasn't given the priority it needed. All this was to change with the explosion of the *Grandcamp* and the disastrous fires that followed. As a direct result of the devastating disaster Community Awareness Response in Emergency teams were set up to warn people of dangerous situations.

This fountain was erected as a memorial to those fire-fighters who died in the Texas City blaze.

Without warning

When the *Grandcamp* caught fire the port authorities should have warned the fire-fighters what was on board, and what the danger was. There should have been an **evacuation**. Instead schoolchildren and dock workers all stood and watched as the **explosive** ship burned. Ken LeMat was president of the Texas City Company Railway which ran the port. He recognized that people should have done more. 'We weren't prepared for the disaster,' he said. 'We lacked communications and there was no-one to take control.'

These survivors of the explosion were lucky and escaped unharmed. The port still holds horrific memories for many people like these.

Compensation

Victims of the Texas City disaster tried to sue the US Coast Guard. They accused them of **negligence**. The Coast Guard should have done more to prevent the disaster, they said. But the US Supreme Court – the highest court in the land – ruled that the Coast Guard, as a government agency, couldn't be held responsible under existing US laws.

It was not until 1955 – eight years after the disaster – that the US Congress passed a new law, and finally paid **compensation** to the victims who had suffered in the Texas City disaster.

Killer Cloud

Gas Cloud Disaster in Bhopal, India

At midnight on 2 December 1984 a deadly cloud of gas leaked from the American-owned Union Carbide **pesticide** factory in the city of Bhopal, India killing 2500 people within a week. It was disaster on a tragic scale. Survivors are still suffering and dying from the effects of the poison.

An accident waiting to happen

A new underground tank had been installed at the Bhopal factory. It was called tank 610 and it held 42 tonnes of a dangerous liquid chemical called methyl isocyanate. This is a 'volatile' chemical meaning that if heated or mixed with air or water it will react violently.

On 1 December engineers at the plant began cleaning pipes above tank 610. They flushed thousands of gallons of water through the system. They weren't doing anything wrong and it should have been safe. But the engineers didn't know that a valve was leaking. Water that should have flushed through the pipes had in fact leaked into tank 610. Inside the tank the water and volatile chemicals began to mix and react dangerously together.

Later, workers noticed water leaking from tank 610. They found that a **pressure gauge** was missing. They guessed it had been blown off by the pressure building up in the tank. At midnight they told the factory boss that gas was leaking into the air.

20

In the factory control room the emergency had become clear. The temperature and pressure in the tank had gone off the scale. Tank 610 was boiling like a kettle, letting off a cloud of poison gas. Workers at the factory were **evacuated**. But for the city of Bhopal there was no warning. A fog of deadly yellow gas began to drift slowly over the city.

After the Bhopal disaster street clinics like this one were set up to treat victims.

Ramesh was a young boy when disaster struck Bhopal. This is his story.

People were shouting, 'Get up, run, run. Gas has leaked!'. My elder brother got up and said, 'Everyone is running away. We must run too.' I opened my eyes and saw the room was full of white smoke.

The moment I took the rug from my face, my eyes started stinging and every breath was burning my insides. I was scared of opening my eyes.

As we reached the main road we could see a lot of people lying around. We did not know whether they were dead or unconscious.

Unfolding Disaster

For three hours the gas continued to leak over Bhopal. People woke to find their houses filled with choking, blinding gas. They did not know what the gas was. Union Carbide, which owned the factory, had never told people what to do in an emergency.

The poison cloud affected 200,000 people in Bhopal. In the darkness there was panic. People ran blindly through the streets trying to escape. Thousands of people crammed into hospitals. Many could not breathe, or had been blinded by the methyl isocyanate gas. By the morning hospitals were overflowing with casualties. There weren't enough hospitals to treat everyone who needed help.

1 Inspectors from Union Carbide visit Bhopal in 1982. They note that the Union Carbide factory is unsafe and would not be allowed in America. There are accidents the next year. A boy dies. But the factory is not made safer.

2 Sometime late in the evening of 2 December 1984, water leaks into tank 610. Temperature and pressure in the tank rise as the water and chemical inside react and begin to boil. The chemical turns into gas and begins to escape from the tank.

3 Two emergency systems should stop gas escaping from tank 610. The first is a filter called a 'scrubber'. It should make the deadly gas harmless. But it doesn't work. Next, a tower should burn gas as it escapes. But the tower is closed for repair.

5 By the early hours of 3 December hospitals are overflowing with injured and dying people. Only the most seriously hurt get treatment because there are not enough drugs or doctors to help everyone. No-one is quite sure what the gas contained, or how to treat the injuries. Bosses at Union Carbide have information about the gas that can help treat the injured but they do not tell doctors or authorities at Bhopal. More people die. Even after 2000 people are dead Union Carbide factory managers are still claiming that the gas was not poisonous.

4 By midnight on 2 December the gas cloud is drifting across Bhopal. People do not know what to do, or where to go. When warning sirens sound the panic and chaos increases.

Shock and Anger

In the hours and days after the gas leak, the people of Bhopal were in a state of shock. Parents and children just wanted to find their families, and bury their dead.

But this shock quickly turned to anger at Union Carbide, the company which owned the factory. Indian people realized that the Union Carbide factory, and the disaster, would never have been allowed to happen in America.

People became so angry that workers who had been at the factory on the night of the disaster had to be given protection. When Warren Anderson, the Chairman of Union Carbide, arrived from America he was arrested by police in Bhopal. He was released later, but it was clear that in Bhopal people wouldn't forget what had happened.

Living with the disaster

Many of those who survived in Bhopal suffered diseases and trauma after the disaster. Many were blinded, and many people's lungs were damaged by breathing the poisonous gas. Yet many people never got the help they needed. Injections that would help people made ill by the gas took seven years to give to everyone who needed them. Money to help survivors and the families of those who had died took months or years to distribute. It took five years before Union Carbide agreed to pay anything to the surviving victims and the amount they paid was much less than an American court would have made the company pay.

Angry protesters demonstrate against Union Carbide.

Perhaps worst of all for the survivors of Bhopal is that the disaster continues to affect them. Between 1000 and 10,000 people have died from the affects of the gas since the disaster. But Union Carbide have tried to re-open the factory, and even today still deny that the disaster caused by their factory was their fault. They say that one worker **sabotaged** the plant on purpose.

Taking care
Disasters often make people realize they should be more careful. This is what many governments and chemical companies realized after the disaster at Bhopal in India. Since 1986 all chemical companies in America have been required to report all leaks and spills of a long list of harmful chemicals. Many chemical companies also spend more money on safety and the **environment**. Today they spend around four per cent of their total sales on safety and the environment. This is four times what they spent before the Bhopal disaster.

Safety and Money

Safety, and controlling pollution, costs money. At Bhopal, and at Minamata, companies decided to save money, rather than spend it. These decisions cost the lives of thousands of people.

Organizations such as **Greenpeace** say that industries should take precautions, not risks. They call this the 'precautionary principle'. Yet this would often mean that the things we buy would become more expensive, because companies that spend money on safety would try to get that back from their customers. Not everyone wants or is able to pay more.

Industry today makes and uses some of the most dangerous substances we have ever known. Sometimes the dangers aren't realized until these chemicals have been in use for years. This is true of a **pesticide** known as DDT. It was sold and used all over the world for decades. But it is now known that, just like any poison, DDT harms people and causes disease. DDT is now banned by many of the world's governments.

This foul-looking fluid is chemically polluted water gushing out from an industrial waste pipe in Merseyside, England.

Technicians wearing protective suits take soil samples at a **toxic** waste area. They can assess how much damage is being done to the environment.

Finding a balance

Governments have the job of finding a balance between cost and safety. They make rules which decide how much a factory can pollute, and what safety systems it should have in order to avoid disaster. But governments often move slowly, as at Minamata. Science and industry moves more quickly into the unknown – and this can be when disasters happen.

An everyday disaster

Pollution from industry and rubbish is an everyday disaster. Although most companies obey strict guidelines, chemicals do end up in the **environment**, and from there find their way into our food and drinking water. Other chemicals are added to our food when it is made or processed. Some cause harm, and some do not, but it is not yet known which are the really dangerous ones.

Waste sites

There are over 30,000 potentially poisonous former industrial waste sites in England and Wales – one every 500 hectares. In the USA there are over 425,000 potentially hazardous waste sites, that is one for every 611 Americans.

The World's Worst Chemical Disasters

Explosion – Texas City, USA, 16 April 1947 An explosion on a ship carrying dangerous chemicals in Galveston Bay costs hundreds of lives. Fires and explosions rage through the city, flattening buildings.

Pollution – Minamata Bay, Japan, 1953–1968 Mercury waste dumped by plastics factory kills 900 people.

Blast – Flixborough, UK, 1 June 1974 A chemical plant exploded killing 55 people and injuring 75.

Poison cloud – Seveso, Italy, 10 July 1976 Poisonous dioxin escaped from a chemical factory. Over 700 people were **evacuated**, 250 people were poisoned. One year later over 400 children became ill.

Poison cloud – Bhopal, India, 2 December 1984 Highly **toxic** gas leaks from the Union Carbide **pesticide** factory. Within a week 2500 people are dead.

Pollution – Basel, Switzerland, 1 November 1986 Thirty tonnes of chemicals were flushed into the River Rhine after a fire at a chemical plant. The river took 10 years to recover.

Global warming

It is hard to know what disasters we are storing up for ourselves in the future. Global warming could be one of them. Global warming is a predicted rise in temperatures around the world. Some scientists say it is already happening. Between 1890 and 1990 the world has become 0.5°C warmer.

Global warming is caused by gases – such as carbon dioxide from car exhausts and industry – that collect high in the Earth's **atmosphere**. Instead of heat from the Sun hitting the Earth and being bounced out again, these gasses trap the heat and return it to Earth. So the world becomes warmer.

If you live in a cold country the idea of the world being a little warmer might not seem such a bad thing. But in reality it would cause all sorts of problems. A warmer Earth would mean the ice-caps at the north and south poles could begin to melt. Sea levels would rise and low-lying countries, such as Bangladesh or Holland, might disappear beneath the sea. Other effects, such as the spread of tropical diseases or pests are very hard to predict – but it is possible that they could happen.

Unfortunately, as with all disasters that haven't yet happened, scientists cannot agree on whether global warming is a real threat to the Earth or not.

Global warming would melt glaciers and icebergs and increase sea levels all over the world.

Glossary

atmosphere blanket of gases which surround Earth

bacteria simplest and smallest form of plant life. They live in large numbers in the air, soil and water.

compensation money paid to make amends for a wrong done to someone

contaminate to pollute something or somewhere with poisonous chemicals

dredge scoop up mud from a channel or river

environment external surroundings; the land, water and air around us

enzymes special proteins that speed up the chemical changes necessary for life

evacuate/evacuation move people away from a dangerous place until the danger is over

explosive chemicals used to make bombs

fertilizer food for plants used by farmers to put on their crops

fumes unpleasant smoke or gas

Greenpeace organization that campaigns to save the environment

negligence lack of proper care and attention

OECD Organization for Economic Co-operation and Development. It is an international organization of which most rich countries are members.

pesticide chemical used to kill or control insects on crops

pressure gauge measure showing the force of steam or air acting inside equipment

raw material original ingredients for a product

refinery place where oil is cleared of impurities (refined)

sabotaged damage done to something on purpose

synthetic any material made from chemicals

toxic poisonous

United Nations association of different countries which work together for international peace and security. It aims to aid refugees, victims of disaster, war and poverty.

World Health Organization agency of the United Nations established in 1946 to help prevent the spread of diseases worldwide

Index